FOOD AND BEVERAGE CONSUMPTION AND HEALTH

FOOD SAFETY AT HOME: THE LAST STEP OF FOOD SUPPLY CHAIN

FOOD AND BEVERAGE CONSUMPTION AND HEALTH

Additional books in this series can be found on Nova's website under the Series tab.

Additional E-books in this series can be found on Nova's website under the E-book tab.

FOOD AND BEVERAGE CONSUMPTION AND HEALTH

FOOD SAFETY AT HOME: THE LAST STEP OF FOOD SUPPLY CHAIN

ANDREJ OVCA
MOJCA JEVŠNIK
KRISTINA LIKAR
AND
PETER RASPOR

Nova Science Publishers, Inc.
New York

For permission to use material from this book please contact us:
Telephone 631-231-7269; Fax 631-231-8175
Web Site: http://www.novapublishers.com

Additional color graphics may be available in the e-book version of this book.

LIBRARY OF CONGRESS CATALOGING-IN-PUBLICATION DATA

Food safety at home : the last step of food supply chain / authors: Andrej Ovca ... [et al.]
p. cm.
Includes index.
ISBN 978-1-61728-487-8 (softcover)
1. Food--Safety measures. 2. Home economics. I. Ovca, Andrej.
TX531.F56823 2011
363.19'26--dc22 2010051545

Published by Nova Science Publishers, Inc. † New York

Contents

Preface		**vii**
Chapter 1	**Introduction**	**1**
Chapter 2	**Food-related Incidents and Outbreaks not Arising from Food Supply Chain**	**5**
Chapter 3	**Consumer as an Equal Part of Food Supply Chain**	**11**
Chapter 4	**Good Housekeeping Practice**	**15**
Chapter 5	**Education and Training**	**23**
Chapter 6	**Conclusion**	**27**
References		**29**
Index		**37**

PREFACE

Due to number of food-related incidents and reported outbreaks worldwide, food quality and food safety have become a hot topic in everyday life. But risk perception research indicates that common people perceive risks differently from experts. Although outbreaks of food poisoning are usually well documented in the media, there is very little attention paid to the outbreaks that occur as consequence of improper food handling at home. Consumers in everyday life often do not respect basic principles of food safety and, as such, at the end of food supply chain, present risk for themselves and their near relatives and friends. Several studies highlighted gaps in food safety knowledge and some critical safety violations regarding food handling at home. Global food safety will be achieved only then, when every single link in the food supply chain will entirely become master of its particular area and will trust in activity of both previous and following link in the food safety circle called food supply chain, not ignoring consumer as the one who should be aware of potential risks, proper handling and preparation of food for safe and balanced everyday meals. Only safety-conscious consumers can become active partners within the food safety circle. In this book , review of consumer studies and their conclusions concerning food safety knowledge and practices will be presented. Also the role and responsibility of consumer as a last link in food supply chain will be discussed.

Chapter 1

INTRODUCTION

"Food safety" is a broader term, which means an assurance that food will not cause harm to the consumer when it is prepared and/or eaten according to its intended use. Providing consumer with safe and healthy food is in the age of globalization linked with different lifestyle of food habits and responsibility and represents a constant task in developed and developing countries. Food safety understanding is a concept that begins with technologies and goes all the way to the legislation, from the producer to the consumer (Raspor, 2004).

The most common causes of hazards along the food supply chain are connected with some biological, chemical or physical parameters that have to be managed. From the available data reported by Food Safety Department, WHO (Rocourt et al., 2003) time/temperature abuse appears to be the most frequent contributing factor in eleven of the Organization for Economic Co-operation and Development (OECD) countries. Factors involved in food-borne diseases represent four main groups (A, B, C, D) of contributing parameters, related to contamination (e.g., cross contamination, improper storage), to survival of micro organisms (e.g., time/temperature abuse), to those related to microbial growth that can contribute to outbreaks (food prepared too far in advance) and other parameters, mostly unknown sources (Figure 1) (Raspor and Jevšnik, 2008).

Food safety is of crucial importance to the consumer, food industry and economy. Despite significant investment, the incidence of FBD still increases. Foodborne diseases caused by microbiological hazards are a public health problem in Europe and worldwide.

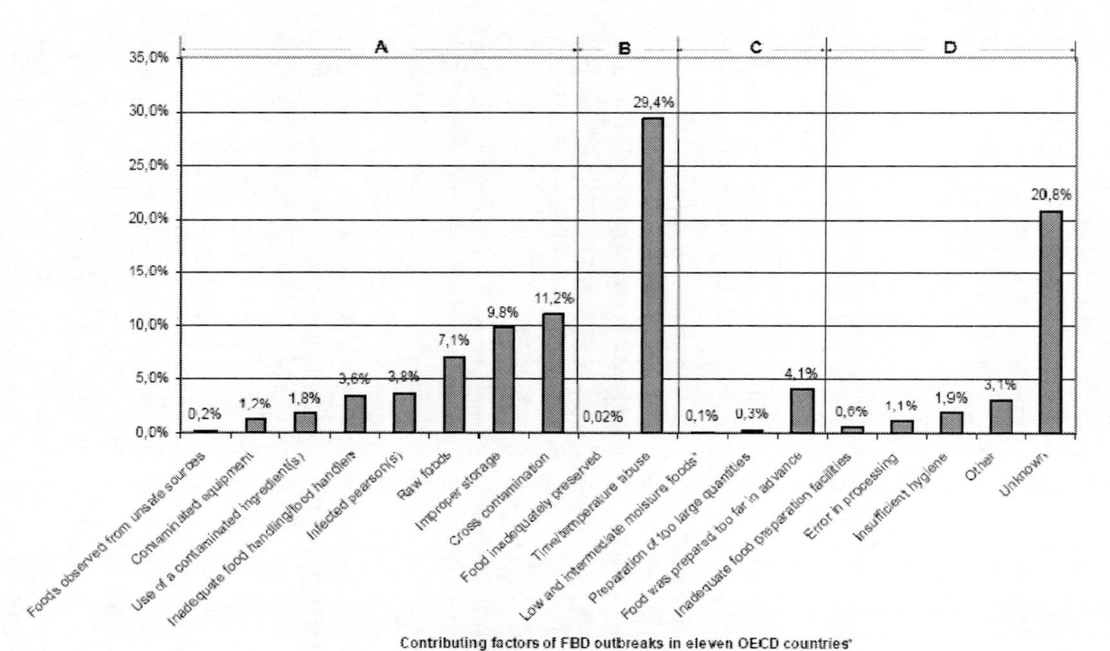

Legend: * Denmark, Finland, France, Hungary, Iceland, Ireland, New Zealand, Slovak Republic, Spain, Sweden, United Kingdom.

Figure 1. Evaluation of FBD outbreaks showed eight parameters connected to contamination (A), two parameters with survival of microbes (B), three parameters with microbial growth (C) and five others (D) which represent 38.6%, 29.4%, 4.5% and 27.5% (Raspor and Jevšnik, 2008; reprinted with permission of the publisher Taylor & Francis Group).

Inability to effectively improve the situation is a matter of major concern in spite of the very significant resources allocated to the problem of food-borne diseases. A closer look to food field, which is spread from technical sciences to social sciences, is giving broad spectrum of possibilities of how to maintain food safety completely, with consumer who stands at the end of the chain. Food safety represents a cross-section of three important fields: food regulation, food technology, analytics, and finally, public food safety knowledge and awareness. The purpose of these three fields is to protect human health. Today, we master food safety with different good practices, which are the consequence of human culture, history and lifestyle. If we analyse good practices in the broad spectrum of food area, we could arrange them in three categories. First, category of good practices is directly connected with food technology (i.e., Good Manufacturing Practice - GMP). Second category is indirectly connected with food issues (i.e., Good Research Practice - GRP, Good Educational Practice - GEP, Good Training Practice - GTrP). The third category deals with all the activities regarding consumers' food handling (Good Housekeeping Practice - GHKP). Finally, the point is that the food safety is not mastered according to concept "From Farm to Fork," because consumers are not properly connected to food supply chain (Raspor and Jevšnik, 2008; Raspor, 2008).

Home food preparers need knowledge and skills for effective food-handling, but also they have to be motivated to act upon that knowledge as preconditions to behaviour change (Medeiros et al., 2004; Redmond and Griffith, 2003). It is obvious that consumers are not provided with sufficient, processed and easy-to-understand information (Banati and Lakner, 2006).

Field of food science and technology is a part of natural science and thus researched mainly with quantitative methodology (Jevšnik et al., 2006). Reliable and valid scientific discoveries are a precondition for achieving the final goal of scientific research, namely discovering legality that enables explanation and subsequently prediction of observed phenomena (Hlebec, 2001). It is understandable that complex behavioural barriers require detailed diagnostic tools and matching interventions to effectively overcome them, especially in the field of food safety. Behavioural research offers an innovative, yet logical, approach to the problems existing within the field of food safety management, and one that has so far been mostly untouched (Gilling, 2001; Gilling et al., 2001). People do not react to outside signals automatically but individually interpret their meaning. That is why it is important to learn in detail about various ways of signal interpretation, which can be done with qualitative research techniques. Quantitative as well as qualitative methodology has its advantages and disadvantages. None of the two methodological techniques can assure completely valid and reliable data, but if combined, they can provide important insights into dynamics of a society. In general, quantitative data offer more static insights but enable research of basic patterns and structures. Qualitative data, on the other hand, is less appropriate for determining patterns and structures in general, but enables more thorough and in-depth understanding of the process of changes in social life (Haralambos and Holborn, 1999). That is why further multidisciplinary food safety research should be encouraged to seize the importance of a human being in units of food chain. Formal and informal organizational structures and relations should be taken into strong consideration. Due to a significant increase in information that scientists from different fields are facing today, a systematic approach to analysis of published discoveries became essential. Multidisciplinary approach, including experts for food safety, food technology, psychology, sociology and public health, is thus of great importance (Jevšnik et al., 2006).

Chapter 2

FOOD-RELATED INCIDENTS AND OUTBREAKS NOT ARISING FROM FOOD SUPPLY CHAIN

Food-borne diseases are associated with microbial pathogens, biotoxins and chemical contaminants in food. According to the WHO definitions, "food-borne disease" is any disease of an infectious or toxic nature caused by the consumption of food, while "food-borne disease outbreak" is classified as the occurrence of two or more cases of a similar food-borne disease resulting from the ingestion of same food. The "food-borne outbreak" is also defined by the European Union Directive 2003/99/EC, as "an incidence, observed under given circumstances, of two or more human cases of the same disease and/or infection, or a situation in which the observed number of human cases exceeds the expected number and where the cases are linked, or are probably linked, to the same food source." Whereas, "food" is defined in Regulation (EC) No 178/20022 as any substance or product, whether processed, partially processed or unprocessed, intended to be, or reasonably expected to be ingested by humans, where this definition includes also drinking water and covers single food items as well as composite meals.

Consumer concern about treats associated with food is growing. Due to recent food crises in Europe, food quality and food safety have become a hot topic in mass media. Food safety is of crucial importance to the consumer, food industry and economy. It is commonly known that the number of food-borne diseases is increasing in both the developed and the developing countries. Calculation of annual cases of salmonellosis and campylobacteriosis shows that the yearly number of cases in Europe is likely to exceed five million, demonstrating that economic losses and human distress resulting from food-borne diseases can no longer be neglected (Raspor, 2004). Food contamination creates an enormous social and economic burden on communities and their health systems. Korel, Ergönül and Gökgöz (2003) reported that in the last 20 years, these economic losses amounted to nearly 1.0–1.2 billion dollars, indicating the importance of food safety and the HACCP system. The incidence of food-borne diseases is rising in developing countries, as well as in the developed world (Redmond and Griffith, 2003). The cause can be found in a better way of life, improved laboratory diagnostics, and an increasing number of infections involving new or more virulent types (Tauxe, 2002; Smole Možina and Hočevar Grom, 2004). According to epidemiologists, the recent emergence of infectious diseases can be considered a third epidemiological transition, characterized by a globalization of human disease ecology and the evolution of considerable technological and social-economic changes. The changing epidemiology of food-borne diseases and the increase in knowledge concerning emerging food-borne pathogens requires a re-examination of food safety educational messages to ensure that the guidance given to consumers is appropriate for controlling pathogens that are prevalent in the food supply chain (Hillers et al., 2003).

Countries with reporting systems have documented significant increases in the incidence of food-borne disease outbreaks during the last two decades (Rocourt et al., 2003) and as shown further, consumer as a last part of food supply chain represents substantial part of these outbreaks.

Globalization of the food supply has led to the rapid and widespread international distribution of foods. Pathogens can be inadvertently introduced into new geographical areas. Changes in microorganisms lead to the constant evolution of new pathogens, development of antibiotic resistance, and changes in virulence of known pathogens (WHO, 2008). The true number of food-related outbreaks is difficult to ascertain because of the fact that a lot of cases with mild symptoms remain unreported especially when they are consequence of improper food handling at home. Often, outbreaks of food-borne disease are unrecognized or unreported or are not investigated (WHO, 2008). Also cases of food-related outbreaks that are not arising from any other link of food supply chain typically affect small number of individuals, which presents another obstacle for public health authorities to identify them. Surveillance data collected by health departments is usually underestimated. Only a proportion of cases are reported to health departments, and this is dependent on several factors including: healthcare-seeking behavior, stool testing practices differing among general practitioners, a patient submitting a stool specimen, the laboratory testing for the pathogen, and the result of testing being reported to public health authorities (The Ozfoodnet Working Group, 2007). In spite of facts listed, up to 87% of reported food-related outbreaks have been associated with food prepared or consumed in the home, while there is quite large range regarding different countries included (Redmond and Griffith, 2003). In the Netherlands, for example, there are an estimated 2 million food-borne diseases every year, of which 30 to 50% are supposed to find their origin in family homes (Oosterom, 1998).

The source of food-borne diseases outbreaks is unknown in most of the reported cases. Foods most frequently involved in outbreaks are eggs and egg products, meat and meat products, and confectionery products, with the likely implication of these foods being associated with *Salmonella* and *Campylobacter* (Raspor & Jevšnik, 2008). Food-borne pathogens such as *Salmonella spp.*, *Campylobacter spp.,* Pathogenic *E. coli* and *Listeria spp.* are commonly present in the numerous raw foods used in domestic kitchen (Jones, 1998) and are also often present on the kitchen surfaces where food is prepared. In study done by Rusin et al. (1998), the kitchen surfaces were even more contaminated, also with the fecal coliforms, than in the bathroom. Therefore, it is not surprising that pathogens listed before, also according to the data presented further, are most frequently isolated cause for food-related outbreaks at home.

Further on, according to the available data, food-related outbreaks that are originating from domestic environment in framework of all reported food-borne outbreaks are presented for Europe, Australia, United States of America and Africa, with emphasis on the latest reports available. However, it should be emphasized that data presented and discussed further is based upon different monitoring systems and cannot be directly compared. Some countries distinguish between domestically acquired cases and cases acquired abroad; also a large part of the observed variation might be accounted for by different diagnostic methods and differences in the surveillance systems and the ways of reporting.

EUROPE

According to the EFSA (European Food Safety Agency) summary report (2009) in year 2007, 5,609 food-borne outbreaks were reported (compared to 5,736 and 4,522 food borne outbreaks in 2006 and 2005, respectively) by EU member states of which 36.1% (2,025) were verified.

The verified outbreaks involved 39,727 people, resulting in 3,291 hospitalizations and causing 19 deaths. In addition, two non-member states reported 93 food-borne outbreaks, of which 38.7% were verified and where 1,475 people were affected, hospitalizing 55 and causing five deaths. France and Spain reported 73.0% of verified outbreaks in the EU. There was great variation among member states in the numbers and proportions of verified outbreaks reported. In total, 66.6% of the verified outbreaks were general outbreaks affecting members of more than one household where 32.0% were household outbreaks and only 1.4% were notified as an unknown type of outbreak. Households were reported as the setting in 37.0% of outbreaks where this information was provided. Regarding food source, domestically produced foodstuffs were reported as the source in 14.6% of verified outbreaks (2,025). Households (61.3%) were reported to be the most important settings in verified *Salmonella* outbreaks, involving a total of 2,390 cases; 25.8% of the cases were admitted to hospital and two cases died. The vast majority of reported settings in verified *Campylobacter* outbreaks were households (52.0%) involving a total of 66 human cases of which eight cases were admitted to hospital. The origin of the foodstuff was only reported in 25.0% of all verified pathogenic *E. coli* outbreaks, and 83.3% of these originated from domestically produced foodstuffs. The origin of the foodstuff was only reported in 10.9% of all verified bacterial toxin outbreaks, and 90.7% of all reported outbreaks originated from domestically produced foodstuffs. The origin of the foodstuff was reported in 27 out of 30 verified parasitic outbreaks, and 90% of all reported outbreaks originated from domestically produced foodstuffs.

AUSTRALIA

In Australia, it has been estimated that there are 5.4 million cases of food-borne disease or conditions that are commonly transmitted by food annually (The Ozfoodnet Working Group, 2007). According to the latest data available in Australia (year 2007), there were 149 outbreaks of food-borne disease (compared to 115 and 102 food-borne outbreaks in 2006 and 2005, respectively) affecting 2,290 people, which resulted in 266 people being hospitalized and five deaths. The most common place where food was prepared in identified outbreaks was in restaurants (38%; 714 persons) and in private residences (11%; 134 persons) on second place. Private residences are on the second place according to the percentage of outbreaks reported, while they are on the fifth place according to the number of affected persons.

There was a wide variety of foods implicated in outbreaks of food-borne disease, although Australian investigators were unable to identify a specific food vehicle in 40% of outbreaks. There were 24 outbreaks associated with eggs (16% of all food-borne outbreaks). These outbreaks affected a total of 629 people and hospitalized 195 people.

USA

In 1999, the Center for Disease Control and Prevention (CDC) estimated that 76 million cases of food-borne disease occur each year in the United States. The great majority of these cases is mild and cause symptoms for only a day or two. Some cases are more serious, and CDC estimates that there are 325,000 hospitalizations and 5,000 deaths related to food-borne diseases each year (FoodNet, 2005). For USA, the latest available annual report is for year 2005 (FoodNet, 2005). The surveillance area included ten sites: Connecticut, Georgia, Maryland, Minnesota, New Mexico, Oregon, and Tennessee, and selected counties in California, Colorado, and New York, which represents 44.9 million persons or 15.2% of the United States population. In 2005, there were 225 outbreaks reported to the national electronic Food-borne Outbreak Reporting System (eFORS). 205 (91%) were known to be food-borne. In 125 (61%) of these outbreaks, the implicated food item was prepared in a restaurant. There is no data available for any other site of outbreak. An etiology was reported for 173 (84%) of the outbreaks, where the most common confirmed etiologies were norovirus (33%) and *Salmonella* (14%).

AFRICA

Only few countries on African continent have food-borne disease surveillance systems. Only Cameroon, Ethiopia, Madagascar, Nigeria, Senegal and South Africa report data to Global Salm Surv, a global network of laboratories and individuals involved in surveillance, isolation, identification and antimicrobial resistance testing of *Salmonella* and other food-borne pathogens (WHO, 2007). According to the fact listed, it is difficult to get such accurate and reliable data as for Europe and Australia. The incidence of food-borne and waterborne diarrhea is estimated at five episodes of diarrhea per child per year (Koesk et al., 2003). The estimated disability adjusted life years lost to food borne and a waterborne diarrhoeal disease is 5.7% - 7.1%, compared to 4.1% globally (WHO, 2003). Several devastating outbreaks of food-borne diseases such as cholera, salmonellosis, entero-haemorrhagic *Escherichia coli*, hepatitis A and acute aflatoxicosis have occurred in a number of African countries in past few years. In the year 2005, there were 34,000 cases of cholera due to contaminated water and food reported in 30 countries, with more than 1,000 deaths (FAO, 2005).

ASIA

Like for Africa, also for Asia it is difficult to get reliable or comparable data in English language. As an example, data obtained by WHO Surveillance Programme for Control of Food-borne Infections and Intoxications in Europe for Russian Federation for the year 1999 and 2000 (latest available) is presented. A total of 9,796 and 10,696 cases of food-borne diseases were notified in 1999 and 2000, respectively. The place where the food was contaminated was identified in all investigated outbreaks. The most frequently reported place was not domestic environment in comparison to Europe and Australia. Schools and kindergartens were most often reported places of outbreak, accounting for 33% and 50% of outbreaks in 1999 and 2000, respectively. Eggs and egg products were the most common food vehicle.

Many other countries (Southeast Asia) are not ready to conduct risk assessment because of the lack of data, needed laboratory infrastructure, and the required know-how to analyze a wide range of contaminants (Othman, 2007).

From data presented, especially for Europe and Australia, it is evident that consumer as a last link in the food supply chain cannot and should not be neglected and must be taken into consideration as an equal and fully responsible part of food supply chain.

Chapter 3

CONSUMER AS AN EQUAL PART OF FOOD SUPPLY CHAIN

Ensuring safe food for the consumer is in the period of globalization, responsibility and constant task in developed and developing countries. Raspor and Jevšnik (2008) recognised the fact that there is no shared definition and understanding of food safety globally due to good practices. We found a variety of dictionary items and interpretation from different perspectives, but the point is, that we do not treat food safety as a food safety cycle "from the farm to the table," because we often focus on it partially (only individual segments of food chain), and we neglect consumers. Each of us is a consumer, no matter at which stage of food chain we enter the safety cycle.

The principal objective of the general and specific hygiene rules is to ensure a high level of consumer protection with regard to food safety (EU, 2004). Foodstuffs can become a risk factor for consumers if they are not handled and treated along the food supply chain in accordance with principles of good practices and the HACCP (Hazarad Analysis and Critical Control Point) system. The food supply chain does not exclude consumers. But the question is whether consumers are sufficiently informed to assure food safety at the end of the food supply chain. Redmond and Griffith (2003) assert that multiple food safety responsibilities are required by consumers, because consumers not only purchase and receive products but also process and provide foods for themselves and for others. They also stressed that the implementation of proper food-handling practices can prevent cases of food-borne disease, and the way in which consumers handle food in the kitchen affects the risk of pathogen multiplication, cross-contamination to other products, and the destruction of pathogens by thorough cooking procedures (Redmond and Griffith, 2003).

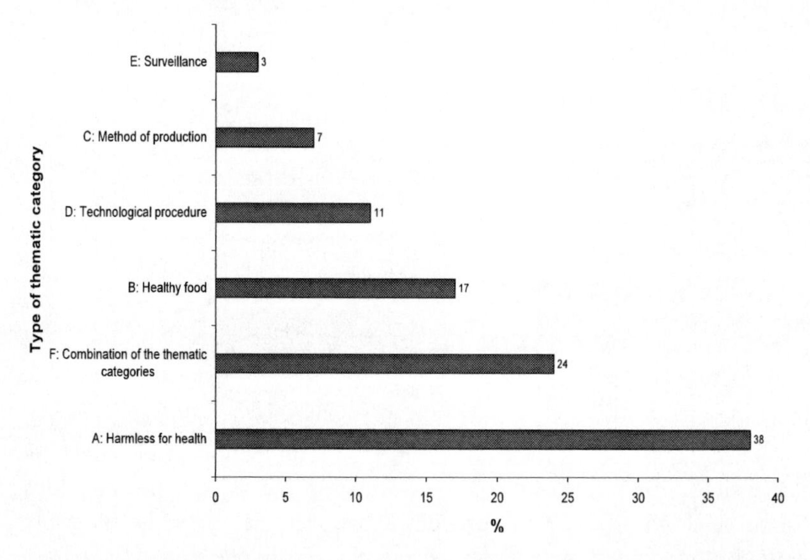

Figure 2. Understanding consumers interpretation of term "Food Safety" (N=920).(Jevšnik et al., 2008c; reprinted with permission of the publisher Akadémiai Kiadó).

What do consumers know about food safety principles and what do they do to protect themselves from food-borne diseases? The meaning of the term "Food Safety" is well known and defined in expert circles, but when we are analysing how it is interpreted by consumers, new dimensions are opening. Jevšnik et al. (2008c) have analysed consumer interpretation of the term "food safety" and classified statements in six categories (Figure 2).

The results of food safety consumer studies concerning knowledge and practices have shown that consumers are aware of and are thinking about food safety, although there are also many gaps in food safety knowledge and practices that may result in food-borne diseases (Jevšnik et al., 2008 a,b,c; Badrie et al., 2006; Medeiros et al., 2004; Patil et al., 2004; Redmond and Griffith, 2003).

Epidemiologic surveillance summaries of diseases clearly indicate that consumer behaviours such as ingestion of raw/undercooked foods and poor hygienic practices are important contributors to outbreaks of food-borne diseases (Patil et al., 2004). Unusan (2007) reported that people of all ages seem to think they know how to handle food safely, but their self-reported food-handling behaviours do not support this confidence. A review of the consumer food safety literature indicates many gaps that have an impact on food-borne diseases at home (Unusan, 2007; Kennedy et al., 2005; Garayoa et al., 2005; Kendall et al., 2004; Redmond and Griffith, 2003; Hillers et al., 2003; Li Cohen and Bruhn, 2002; Yang et al., 2000; Jay et al., 1999a,b). Wilcock et al. (2004) assert that, overall, consumer attitudes towards food safety in general differ according to demographic and socio-economic factors such as gender, age, educational level and economic status. Consumers need to know which behaviours are most likely to result in illness in order to make decisions about food handling and consumption behaviours (Hillers et al., 2003), and then need to be motivated to act on that knowledge as a precondition for behavioural change (Medeiros et al., 2004).

It is very important to investigate a consumer's knowledge, behaviour and attitudes toward food safety. Redmond and Griffith (2003) noted that target social marketing of food safety strategies is required because they found differences in perceived responsibility between males and females and consumers from different age groups. They also emphasised that consumers need to perceive interventions as personally relevant for there to be effective food safety education.

An important perspective is to educate the public about safe food handling and preparation of foods throughout the system of good nutritional practice that emphasizes hazardous food-handling techniques and the microbiological causes of food-borne disease.

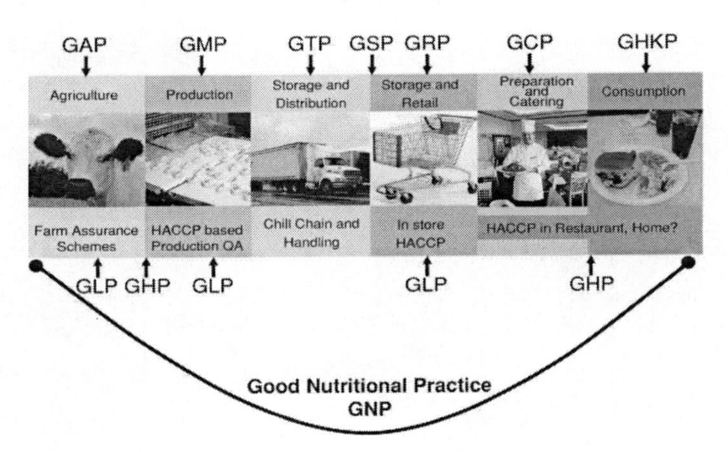

Figure 3. Good Nutrition Practice (GNP) interlinking relevant good practices including Good Housekeeping practice in food supply chain (Raspor and Jevšnik, 2008;reprinted with permission of the publisher Taylor & Francis Group).

Chapter 4

GOOD HOUSEKEEPING PRACTICE

To achieve global food safety, consumers should be well informed regarding basic principles of food safety practice at homes (Good Housekeeping Practice), because food safety begins and ends at consumer daily practice (Raspor and Jevšnik, 2008).

To achieve adequate food safety, a coordinated plan is needed for all involved in the food chain, including primary and secondary production, distributors, and consumers (Garoyoa et al., 2005). Jones (1998) stressed that it is by all means important to pay attention to hygienic measures and that they can decrease numerous potential risk factors, which stresses the importance of acknowledging HACCP principles also at home (Griffith and Worsfold, 1994; Beumer, 2003). In the last twenty years, most of the work has been centred on hazard control in the production sector, but the government has not dedicated the same effort to improving food safety education of consumers. Effective risk communication to inform consumers of the possible health risks of food-borne illnesses and encouraging safer food-handling practices in the home is probably the best way to ensure food safety at the consumer end of the food chain (Patil et al., 2005).

The importance of restoring the systems based on analysis of all relevant practices contributing to food safety has been stressed along the principles: "From stable to table," "From farm to fork," "From spring to drink" (Raspor, 2004; Raspor, 2006). In classical food chain strategy, all relevant activities are taken for benefit of human beings but locating consumer outside the system. The consumer should be an integral part of food safety systems because it is a vital link between retail and home. We expected that a well-developed consumer would start to obey "Good Housekeeping Practice" (GHKP). GHKP is selection of the principles and techniques of food storage and preparation at home performed directly by consumers. According to considerable number of food-borne diseases occurring in domestic food preparation, it is obvious that we do not have GHKP and we neglect fact that the consumer makes a crucial link in food supply chain. Consumer behavior and attitudes toward food safety shows that the levels of understanding, motivation and trust needs to be further cultivated and raised. It has been shown that present maintenance of food safety in food chain can be easily broken down, because of different kind of barriers or simple misunderstanding. Therefore a new approach called "Good Nutritional Practice" (GNP) should be adopted to balance food safety. It is important to restoring the existent food safety system with GNP, based on a model (Figure 3) that covers subsystems from other good practices (Raspor and Jevšnik, 2008; Raspor, 2008).

Jones (1998) warned about focusing on particular (sensitive) groups and proposed to apply HACCP to identify hygiene risks in the home. She suggested drawing up hygiene codes of practices and thus forming the basis of educational material aimed at different target groups. International studies indicated that a significant proportion of food-borne diseases arises from practices in the home kitchen (Scott et al., 1982; Bryan, 1988; Scott, 1996; Wilcock et al., 2004; Patil et al., 2004; Unusan, 2007; Jevšnik et al., 2008 a,b,c,d,). Domestic food preparation can negate much of the efforts of primary and secondary food producers to provide safe food (Oosterom, 1998; Jay et al., 1999a,b). The fact is that household food safety education is needed to minimize the risk of exposure to food-borne pathogens.

4.1. PURCHASING

For food safety in stores, food producers and sellers are responsible. The proper handling of food during the purchase and after is, as already mentioned, the responsibility of each consumer himself. During the purchase, consumers estimate different parameters of the purchasing differently. Two studies (Jevšnik et al., 2008a; Surujlal and Badrie, 2004) reported that respondents most often check the date of durability and the state of packaging, where women and younger respondents significantly more often check the date of durability than men and older respondents respectively. The least important parameter for consumers during the purchase is temperature in a retail cold chain unit, where it needs to be considered that consumers simply trust shop managers or they assume that they cannot influence the temperature settings. Consumer trust to the shop managers was confirmed also by another study done by Ovca and Jevšnik (2009), where respondents who first strongly agreed with the statement that the proper storage temperature of foods is very important, then in the further area admitted that they almost never noticed the temperature control of cold chain units by retailers in spite of fact that they are obligated to control temperature in their cold chain units.

To avoid possible irregularities that could affect the food safety and also food quality, consumers should always carefully read declaration and follow the manufacturer's instructions. With packaged foods, consumer need be attentive that the packaging is intact, while in case of unwrapped foods, they need to be sensitive for the sensory properties like their appearance, smell and freshness. Also important is the order of purchasing different products where perishable food items should be taken last before leaving the store to reduce the potential temperature abuse. Jay et al. (1999b) found out that more than half of Australian consumers included in the survey (58.3%) of respondents bought their raw meat at the end of their shopping trip, which is much better than the situation reveled by Jevšnik et al. (2008a), where only 10% of consumers included in the survey act that way. In general, consumers put the perishable food items like raw meat in their shopping basket when they came across it (Jevšnik et al. 2008a; Ovca and Jevšnik, 2009), therefore arrangement of different shopping areas in stores can have significant impact on the consumers' order of purchasing different items.

4.2. Food Safety Practice from Purchase to Home

Transport to the home should be as short as possible, which is especially important in case of perishable and sensitive foods, which must be stored at low temperatures. Similar behavior is also important in the purchase of sensitive fruit and vegetables like strawberries, grapes, tomatoes, etc. Proper time of transport is, therefore, an important factor for bacterial growth beside temperature, which is crucial. Already, the survey done by Evans et al. (1991) has shown that consumers take between two and 510 minutes to transport chilled foods from retail stores to their homes and up to a further 90 minutes to empty their car or shopping bags and place the products in refrigerators. Recent study (Jevšnik et al., 2008a) revealed that the average time consumers need from store to their home is 25 minutes (SD=18.4), where some other studies revealed that 7% of consumers included in the survey need more than 90 minutes (Kennedy et al., 2005), and 5.8% more than 60 minutes (Jay et al., 1999b). Of course, we need to be aware that there are many factors influencing the time of transport, which are of geographic and socio economical origin. According to the guidelines for food stores, rise of food temperature for 3°C in 30-minute intervals should not present significant threat regarding microbiological growth. Besides time, the way of transport is also important. Consumers should not expose food to direct sunlight; therefore, if the transport is done by car, it is recommended to store food during the transport in the car boot. A clean container is essential to avoid contamination of food and to prevent changes in of sensory properties, especially adsorption of foreign smells. To avoid undesirable storage conditions, it is recommended that the purchase of food is the last assignment before going home. To reduce risk of temperature abuse in case of perishable food items, transport in an insulated bag or box is recommended. The study done by Jevšnik et al. (2008a) revealed that more than half (51.7%) of the consumers included never thought of using a insulated bag, while additional 33% believed that a insulated bag is not even necessary. Among all respondents (N= 985), only 15.5% had ever taken an insulated bag to the store when buying perishable foodstuffs, where this percentage was significantly higher among respondents who believed that the consumer is responsible for food safety ($p = 0.017$). That an insulated bag is not important for one-third of sampled consumers was found out also by Jay et al. (1999b). Evans (1994) investigated the affect of time period and the way of transport on a food temperature purchased from a large retail store and placed in a pre-cooled insulated box or left in the boot of a car unprotected. Some product temperatures placed in the boot rose up to 40°C during a one-hour car journey, where most of the samples placed in the insulated box did not change their temperature during the transport. Those transported in a boot of a car required then approximately five hours after being placed in a domestic refrigerator before the temperature was reduced again below 7°C. In addition to all percussion steps, valuable information regarding bacterial growth during the transport can be obtained with help of predictive modeling. The main objective of predictive modeling is to predict, mathematically, the probability of specific microorganisms' growth and survival in food under known environmental conditions.

4.3. FOOD HANDLING PRACTICES AT HOME

The results of consumer studies concerning food safety knowledge and practices and attitudes toward food safety have shown that consumers are aware of and are thinking about food safety, although there are also many gaps in food safety knowledge and practices that may result in food-borne diseases (Jevšnik et al., 2008a,b,c; Badrie et al., 2006; Medeiros et al. 2004; Patil et al., 2004; Wilcock et al., 2004; Redmond and Griffith, 2003). International studies have shown that a significant proportion of food-borne diseases arise from improper practices in the home kitchens. Domestic food preparation can negate most of the efforts of primary and secondary food producers to provide safe food. Several studies assessing different kinds of consumer groups identified food prepared in the family home as a major source of food poisoning (Sammarco et al., 1997; Johnson et al., 1998; Jay et al., 1999a,b; Meer and Misner, 2000; Leitch et al., 2001; Bermúdez-Millán et al., 2004; Anderson et al., 2004; Marklinder et al., 2004). Many studies highlighted some gaps in food safety knowledge and practices that occur from shopping to eating and the need to promote improved food safety behaviours for particular target groups, especially for children, elderly people, pregnant women and immune-compromised people.

. Redmond and Griffith (2003) assumed that the majority of unsafe food hygiene practices observed in the reviewed studies were associated with cross-contamination. Jevšnik et al. (2008a,b) stressed that consumers are not familiar with their role in the food safety chain, and that they allow numerous opportunities for microbiological contamination of food. The most important issues were incorrect defrosting practices, poor cooling of cooked food, re-heating of cooked food, lack of knowledge regarding refrigeration temperatures, lack of knowledge concerning cross-contamination and its control, and a lack of knowledge with respect to hand hygiene (Jevšnik et al., 2008a,b; Redmond and Griffith, 2003). Redmond and Griffith (2003) concluded that knowledge, attitudes, intentions, and self-reported practices did not correspond to observed behaviours, suggesting that observational studies provide a more realistic indication of the food hygiene action actually used in domestic food preparation.

Consumers need to know which behaviours are most likely to result in illness in order to make decisions about food handling and consumption behaviours (Hillers et al., 2003), and then need to be motivated to act on that knowledge as a precondition for behavioural change (Medeiros et al., 2004).

It follows that consumers are one of the important components in the food safety chain when considering a "From Farm to Table" approach.

According to Sammarco et al. (1997), it is essential to understand consumers' awareness regarding home food safety and home food preparation practices in order to plan proper education programs.

4.4. Cold Chain Maintaining

As generally in food supply chain, also on the area of cold chain, maintaining a lot of attention is focused on certain parts of the food supply chain (from farmer or producer to the retailer), while consumer is often overlooked. Consumer food safety regarding perishable food items depends on temperature control throughout all stages in the food supply chain: production, transport, storage, retail display and domestic refrigeration, but temperature measurements taken in stores (Likar and Jevšnik, 2006; Jevšnik, et al., 2008d) clearly show that the cold chain is frequently broken even before perishable food items reach the consumer.

Refrigerated foods represent one of the fastest growing sectors of the grocery and foodservice industries (Tom, 2006; Coulomb, 2008), and at a time of globalization when some foods that require a specific storage temperature regimes travel long distances before reaching the consumer, the maintenance of a cold chain becomes more and more important. Maintaining a required or declared storage temperature for perishable foodstuffs is a key factor in preventing risks, which can affect food safety and food quality.

Refrigeration storage is one of the most widely practiced methods of controlling microbial growth in perishable foods and to prevent outbreaks of food-borne diseases. Jackson and others (2007) continued the work of the Mintel International Group, showing that foodstuffs stored at low temperatures (chilled and frozen foods) and products that can be consumed without further heat treatment represented more than 60% of the typical shopping basket of an average European consumer, while, on the other hand, many foodstuffs (fruit and vegetables, dairy products, meat, fish and seafood) that need to be refrigerated in order to be preserved as a matter of fact, less than 10% of such perishable foodstuffs are refrigerated (Coulomb, 2008).

It is important that the process of maintaining a cold chain does not conclude with the retailer. Maintaining a cold chain should continue up to and within a consumer's home. The methods of handling and storing frozen and chilled foods by the consumer at home can have significant effects on the quality and safety of food products at the end of food supply chain. The refrigerator is a common and one of the most popular household devices in the developed world and very few households do not own a refrigerator or fridge-freezer for the storage of chilled foodstuffs (James et. al., 2008; Bansal, 2003). There are now about one billion domestic refrigerators worldwide, and this is twice as many as one decade ago (Coulomb, 2008). But the findings of James et al. (2008) and many other studies that they review show that domestic refrigerators throughout the world operate above the recommended temperatures and are not properly maintained (Johnson et al., 1998).

Nauta and coworkers (2003) showed that refrigerator temperatures in northern countries of Europe are usually lower than those recorded in southern countries, which is a consequence of external climate conditions and improper setting of refrigerator cooling degree. Improper operating temperatures of domestic refrigerators are, as further examined by Azevedo et al. (2005) and Jackson et al. (2007), in good correlation with the presence of pathogens, especially *Listeria monocytogenes* on surfaces inside of such domestic refrigerators. Baar et al. (2005) and James et al. (2008), therefore, indicated that the household food storage process is perhaps one of the most critical parts of the cold chain maintenance. On the other hand, consumer customs regarding actions taken in context of cold chain maintaining at their domestic environment are far from ideal. The following studies (Anderson et al., 2004; Badrie et al., 2006; Jevšnik et al., 2008a,b; Likar and Jevšnik, 2006; Marklinder et al., 2004; McCarthy et al., 2007; Terpstra et al., 2005; Redmond and Griffith, 2003), which examined food safety practices, revealed that the level of knowledge possessed by consumers regarding the cold chain maintenance is insufficient. Consumers do not possess adequate knowledge about right refrigeration temperatures, and they do not control the temperature at their domestic refrigerators. Therefore, it is not surprising that large proportion of consumers´ refrigerators operate above the recommended temperatures as already mentioned. Consumer behavior and customs regarding cold chain maintaining can be also affected by their life status. According to Jevšnik et al. (2008b), the majority of the women always put foodstuffs that required the maintenance of a cold chain (e.g., fresh meat, dairy products) into the home refrigerator as soon as possible after purchase, but this task was more frequently performed by pregnant women ($p < 0.001$).

Of course, we cannot expect that things will improve thorough the night, but an important improvement of the current situation would occur if consumers understood the necessity of having at least one thermometer in the refrigerator and using it to keep track of temperature, as already suggested by Marklinder et al. (2004).

Chapter 5

EDUCATION AND TRAINING

The results obtained from consumer food safety studies revealed the need for consumer education regarding safe food handling practices from the point of purchase to the home, as well as within the home. We have to educate consumers so that they can cope with all novelties (Raspor, 2006) in the field of food safety on a daily basis.

The attitudes of consumers towards food safety and their practices concerning food are themes of interest to food producers and retailers, public authorities and health educators (Wilcock et al., 2004). Food safety agencies around the globe should play an important role in the education of consumers. Educational material about Good Housekeeping Practice should be available to the general public from many sources. Food safety messages should focus on the younger members of a population with educational programs, but more importantly, with relevant training. It is also of vital importance to properly educate educators and teachers in order to transmit food hygiene principles to children, and through them, to their parents. Only safety-conscious consumers can become active partners within the food safety circle (Raspor and Jevšnik, 2008; Raspor, 2008).

As part of the global strategy to decrease the burden of food-borne diseases, WHO identified the need to communicate a simple global health message, rooted in scientific evidence, to educate all types of food handlers, including ordinary consumers. The Five Keys to Safer Food message, and associated training materials, were developed to provide countries with materials that are easy to use, reproduce and adapt to different target audiences. Prevention of food-borne disease is based on "Five keys to safer food," which includes the following instructions: Keep clean; Separate raw and cooked; Cook thoroughly; Keep food at safe temperatures; Use safe water and raw materials. The Five Keys to Safer Food have been adopted and adapted by over 90 countries and serve as the basis for educational programmes for health educators, food handlers, school children, women and other target audiences involved in food preparation and handling (WHO, 2009).

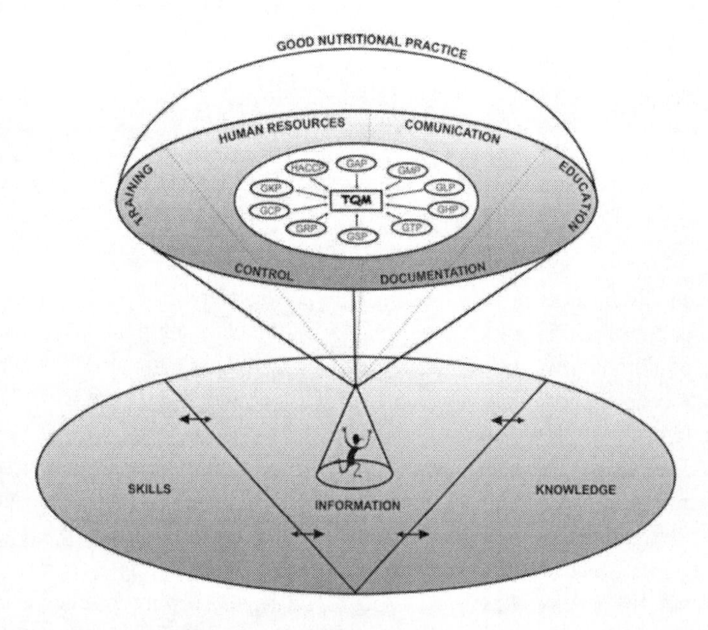

Figure 4. Food safety platform: balance model for ensuring food safety from Good Nutritional Practice viewpoint (Raspor and Jevšnik, 2008 reprinted with permission of the publisher Taylor & Francis Group).

Consumer attitudes and consumer behaviour towards food have been studied by applying approaches such as the Ajzen–Fishbein model of reasoned action and the health belief models (Axleson and Brinberg, 1989; Conento and Murphy, 1990). Wilcock et al. (2004) assert that these approaches argue that individuals make rational decisions about health behaviour when they are aware of associated health problems, have some knowledge concerning these problems, and have some judgement as to the level of risk involved in not changing their behaviour. Thus, the willingness to change behaviour is determined by perceptions and beliefs. In order to change, people have to perceive that their current behaviour endangers their health and that taking action has a strong likelihood of reducing their risk.

Through food safety research review, Redmond and Griffith (2003) demonstrated that substantional proportion of population of Europe, North America, Australia, and New Zeland appear to lack knowledge of key safe food-handling behaviours. Therefore, they warn that consumers may not even be aware that they are implementing unsafe practices. Although perceptions of the risk of food-borne disease appear to be generally accurate, a considerable number of consumers have demonstrated optimistic bias, which may impede attempts to improve food-handling practices through education.

We can conclude that consumer behaviour and attitudes toward food safety have shown that the levels of understanding, motivation and trust need to be further cultivated. It has been shown that present maintenance of food safety in food supply chain can be easily broken down, because of different kind of barriers or simple misunderstanding. Therefore, a new approach called "Good Nutritional Practice" (GNP) was coined to manage food safety. It is important to reconstruct the existent food safety system with GNP, which includes consumers, and is based on a model that covers subsystems from other good practices (Raspor and Jevšnik, 2008), since managing all food issues is a complex and highly demanded issue. Clustering all food safety practices in proper ratio under shield of GNP has been shown to be the appropriate platform for achieving final goal with consumer, namely gastronomic satisfaction, enjoyment with complete support of safety (Raspor, 2008). However in daily practice, most of the critical points are based on particular person on particular place. If we do not perform adequate training and appropriate education within human resources, we cannot expect to have well-informed consumers and professionals with highly developed skills or high knowledge that makes relevant control and documentation through food supply chain. And this is the global goal of GNP based on comprehensive platform, which includes all needed instrument and all partners but also respecting consumer as critical element in this philosophy. Global food safety will be achieved only than when every single link in the food chain will entirely (in its indoor and outdoor environment) become master of its particular area and will trust in activity of both previous and following link in food supply chain. That is why GNP must become a link in the global vision of food safety control, which begins and ends in the concern of consumer (Raspor and Jevšnik, 2008). In Figure 4 is presented new concept called "Good Nutritional Practice," which consists of good practices interlinked with Good Housekeeping Practice.

It is obvious that food represents one of the major problems in the present age next to health and environmental problems. We can expect this trend to continue in the future. Development of new techniques and methods will definitely help us to reduce (avoid) certain hazards and maintain the quality of life; however, we should not forget basic principles of nature. We should make knowledge, constant education and exchange of information our priorities. The trend "from farm to table" is a philosophy with single important goal: safe food on our tables, after all, we are all consumers at the end. To assure it, we should take a critical standpoint and focus on traceability from the beginning to the end and vice versa.

The goal can be achieved only with global co-operation with all who are involved in different kind of food activities: government, teachers and professors, controller's producers, food processors, transporters and trade, catering and ourselves – consumers who stand at the end of the chain. The consumer is the one who should be aware of potential risks, proper handling and preparation of food leading to safe and balanced everyday meals.

Chapter 6

CONCLUSION

Food safety at home if we consult current legislation for a large majority of populations around the globe, the last step of food supply chain is not considered in that perspective. The legislation is not directly connected to the last step of food supply chain at all. Processing and packing inventions and development constantly change food items, not just sensorial part also their nourishing characteristics, which will continue in the future. However, common education is not synchronized with this fast development. If we analyze speed of changes in this area in the last century, we will see that the helix is climbing faster and faster. If the electric stove needed 50 years to be spread globally, refrigerators needed less, and microwave ovens even less. All mentioned equipment changed substantially in the last step in food storage, preparation and consumption. Education has been constantly behind with basic, clear unambiguous information about safe utilization for different layers of people.

It is expected that for the future, we will need even to enhance research and development and will be strongly connected to consumer's basic needs. Analyzing relations, it seems that social sciences do not have much connection to technical and natural sciences, and practically, we only have sporadic connections with consumers, which we pushed in the same cluster of characteristics although it is more than clear that they are extremely different and they hardly have any issue in common, except the need to eat. On one side, "omics" are creating the food/nutrition scientific domain, and on the other, we face nutritional misapprehension, known as obesity, and it is already a safety concern of developed world.

Research and development should be systematically designed on the way to handle food supply chain technically from food farming, food processing, food preservation, food storage and distribution and food consumption, and also in the society to integrate in the system sociological dimension via food security, lifestyle, conception of the world, philosophy of life, religion, policy-making and other soft issues, which dominantly control consumers' behavior during their lifespan.

Currently, food systems still represent a historical collection of knowledge and skills, which are necessary to handle food "From stable to table" "From farm to fork," "From spring to drink." The system of relevant good practices contributing to food quality and safety is not an integral part of systems approach, as we have shown. This will be established scientifically in relevant disciplines that create food knowledge like food science, medical science and consumer science. All this will bring in the future new platforms for communication, which will establish a conscious consumer who will be able to respect good nutritional practice in daily practice. Food producers will become an intelligent interface for tomorrow's consumer in the developed and educated world. This is why we should build on synchronization of novelties in food supply chain with education systems. This is going too slow. Even more, this knowledge and practice is historically allocated in the fields of agronomy, economy, food technology, medicine, microbiology, nutrition, and veterinary medicine and is not integrated on the way to build food systems. It can be foreseen that the era of systems coined by biology systems will create nutrition systems, which will be reflected in good nutritional practice on the applied level and will support the future consumer through his or her lifespan not giving the flavor that person is too old for novelties of modern food supply chain of tomorrow.

References

Axleson, M.L. & Brinberg, D. (1989). *A social-psychological perspective on food-related behaviour.* New York: Springer-Verlag, 190 pp.

Anderson, J.B., Shuster, T.A., Hansen, K.E., Levy, A.S. & Volk, A. (2004). A camera's view of consumer food-handling behaviours. *American Dietetic Association,* 104, 186–191.

Azevedo, I., Regalo, M., Mena, C., Almeida, G., Carneiro, L., Teixeira, P., Hogg, T. & Gibbs, P.A. (2005). Incidence of Listeria spp. in domestic refrigerators in Portugal. *Food Control,* 16, 121–124.

Baar, C., Sebok, A., Horvath, E., Percsi, S., Hegyi, A. & Campden, T.K. (2005). Storage conditions and consumer handling practices of processed meat products in household refrigerators. *Project Grant No. GVOP – 3.1.1. – 2004-05-0152/3.0.* National Office of Research and Technology (NKTH) of the Hungarian Republic.

Badrie, N., Gobin, A., Dookeran, S. & Duncan, R. (2006). Consumer awareness and perception to food safety hazards in Trinidad, West Indies. *Food Control,* 17, 370–377.

Banati, D. & Lakner, Z. (2006). Knowledge and acceptance of genetically modified foodstuffs in Hungary. *Journal of Food and Nutrition Research,* 45(2), 62–68.

Bansal, P.K. (2003). Developing new test procedures for domestic refrigerators: harmonisation issues and future needs – a review. *International Journal of Refrigeration,* 26, 735–748.

Bermúdez-Millán, A., Perez-Escamilla, R., Damio, G., Gonzalez, A. & Segura-Perez, S. (2004). Food safety knowledge, attitudes, and behaviours among Puerto Rican caretakers living in Hartford, Connecticut. *Journal of Food Protection,* 67(3), 512–516.

Beumer, R.R. (2003). Kitchen hygiene in daily life. *International Biodeterioration and Biodegradation,* 51, 299–302.

Bryan, F. (1988). Risks of practices, procedures, and processes that lead to outbreaks of food-borne diseases. *Journal of Food Protection,* 51, 663–673.

CDC (2005) Fodborne illness. Available on line: http://www.cdc.gov/ncidod/dbmd/diseaseinfo/foodborneinfections_g.htm#howmanycases (29. 11. 2009)

Clayton, D.A. & Griffith, C.J. (2003). An investigation of the factors underlying consumers′ implementation of specific food safety practices. *British Food Journal,* 105(7), 434–453.

Conento, I.R. & Murphy, B.M.W. (1990). Psycho-social factors differentiation: people who reported making desirable changes in their diets from those who did not. *Journal of Nutritional Education,* 22, 6–14.

Coulomb, D. (2008). Refrigeration and cold chain serving the global food industry and creating a better future: two key IIR challenges for improved health and environment. *Trends in Food Science and Technology,* 19, 413–417.

Directive 2003/99/EC of the European Parliament and of the Council of 17 November 2003 on the monitoring of zoonoses and zoonotic agents, *amending Council Decision 90/424/EEC and repealing Council Directive* 92/117/EEC, OJ L 325, p. 31.

EFSA (2009) *Trends and Sources of Zoonoses and Zoonotic Agents in the European Union* in 2007. pp. 313.

Ergönül, B. & Günç, P. (2004). Application of HACCP system in catering sector in Turkey. *Internet Journal of Food Safety,* 3, 20–24. Available on line: http://www.internetjfs.org/articles/ijfsv3-5.pdf.

Evans, J.A., Stanton, J.I., Russell, S.L. & James, S.J. (1991). *Consumer handling of chilled foods: a survey of time and temperature conditions.* Ministry of Agriculture Fisheries and Food, Food Science Division II, UK.

Evans, J.A. (1994). The cool option. *XIV International Home Economics and Consumer Studies Research Conference Sheffield,* 21-22 July 1994.

EU (European Union) (2004). Corrigendum to Regulation (EC) No. 852/2004 of the European Parliament and of the Council of 29 April 2004 on the hygiene of foodstuffs (OJ L 139, 30.4.2004). *Off. Journal L226,* 25/06/2004, 3–21.

FAO (2005) Food-borne diseases are a serious threat in Africa. Available on line: http://news.mongabay.com/2005/1003-fao.html (19. 12. 2009).

FoodNet (2005). FoodNet surveillance Report 2005. Available on line: http://www.cdc.gov/foodnet/annual/2005/2005_AR_Report.pdf (21. 12. 2009).

Garayoa, R., Cordoba, M., Garcia-Jalon, I., Sanchez-Villlegas, A. & Vitas, A.I. (2005). Relationship between consumer food safety knowledge and reported behavior among students from health sciences in one region of Spain. *Journal of Food Protection*, 68(12), 2631–2636.

Gilling, S.J., Taylor, E.A., Kane, K. & Taylor, J.Z. (2001). Successful hazard analysis critical control point implementation in the United Kingdom: understanding the barriers through the use of a behavioural adherence model. *Journal of Food Protection,* 64 (5), 710-715.

Gilling, S. (2001). Is your HACCP dragging you down? A psychological perspective. *Food Science & Technology,* 15 (3), 44-47.

Griffith, C.J. & Worsfold, D. (1994). Application of HACCP to food preparation practices in domestic kitchens. *Food Control,* 5(3), 200–204.

Haralambos, M. & Holborn, M. (1999). *Sociology: themes and perspectives.* 2nd ed., Unwin Hyman; London, 594 pp.

Hlebec, V. (2001). Meta-analiza zanesljivosti anketnega merjenja socialne opore v popolnih omrežjih. (Meta-analysis of reliability of network measurement instruments for measuring social support in complete networks). *Teor. praksa,* 38 (1), 63-76.

Hillers, V.N., Medeiros, L., Kendall, P., Chen, G. & DiMascola, S. (2003). Consumer food-handling behaviours associated with prevention of 13 foodborne illnesses. *Journal of Food Protection,* 66(10), 1893-1899.

Jackson, V., Blair, I. S., McDowell, D. A., Kennedy, J. & Bolton, D. J. (2007). The incidence of significant food borne pathogens in domestic refrigerators. *Food Control,* 18, 346–351.

James, S. (1996). The Chill Chain "from Carcass to Consumer" *Meat Science,* 43(S), S203-S216.

James, S.J., Evans, J. & James, C. (2008). A review of the performance of domestic refrigerators. *Journal of Food Engineering,* 87, 2–10.

Jay, L.S., Comar, D. & Govenlock, L.D. (1999a). A video study of Australian domestic food-handling practices. *Journal of Food Protection,* 62(11), 1285–1296.

Jay, L.S., Comar, D. & Govenlock, L. D. (1999b). A national Australian food safety telephone survey. *Journal of Food Protection*, 62(8), 921–928.

Jevšnik, M., Hlebec, V. & Raspor, P. (2006). Meta-analysis as a tool for barriers identification during HACCP implementation to improve food safety. *Acta Alimentaria,* 35(3), 319-353.

Jevšnik, M., Hlebec, V. & Raspor, P. (2008a). Consumers' awareness of food safety from shopping to eating. *Food Control,* 19, 737 – 745.

Jevšnik, M., Hoyer, S. & Raspor, P. (2008b) Food safety knowledge and practices among pregnant and non-pregnant women in Slovenia. *Food Control,* 19, 526–534.

Jevšnik, M., Hlebec, V. & Raspor, P. (2008c). Consumer interpretation of the term food safety. *Acta alimentaria,* 37(4), 437–448.

Jevšnik, M., Ovca, A. & Likar, K. (2008d). Maintaining a cold chain in retail: Does it work? In: SELVAN, N. Kalai (Ed.). *Supply chain management in food industry.* Punjagutta: Icfai University Press, 49 – 68.

Jol, S., Kassianenko, A., Wszol, K. & Oggel, J. (2006). Issues in time and temperature abuse of refrigerated foods. *Food Safety Magazine,* 11(6), 30–35.

Jones, M.V. (1998). Aplication of HACCP to identify hygiene risks in the home. *International Biodeterioration and Biodegradation,* 41, 191 – 199.

Johnson, A.E., Donkin, A.J., Morgan, K., Lilley, J.M., Neale, R.J., Page, R.M. & Silburn, R. (1998). Food safety knowledge and practice among elderly people living at home. *Journal of Epidemiology and Community Health,* 52(11), 745–748.

Kendall, P.A., Elsbernd, A., Sinclair, K., Schroeder, M., Chen, G., Bergmann, V., Hillers, V.N. & Medeiros, L.C. (2004). Observation versus self-report: validation of a consumer food behaviour questionnaire. *Journal of Food Protection*, 67(11), 2578–2586.

Kennedy, J., Jackson, V., Blair, I.S., McDowell, D.A., Cowan, C. & Bolton, D. J. (2005). Food safety knowledge of consumers and the microbiological and temperature status of their refrigerators. *Journal of Food Protection*, 68(7), 1421–1430.

Koesk, M. Bern, C, Guerrant, R.L. (2003). The global burden of diarrhoel disease, as estimated from studies published between 1992 and 2000, *Bulletin of the World Health Organization* 81, 197–204.

Korel, F., Ergönül, B. & Gökgöz, E. (2003). Economic impacts of HACCP system applications in food industry. *Food,* 2003/01, 80–82.

Li-Cohen, A.E., & Bruhn, C.M. (2002). Safety of consumer handling of fresh produce from the time of purchase to the plate: a comprehensive consumer survey. *Journal of Food Protection,* 65(8), 1287–1296.

Likar, K. & Jevšnik, M. (2006). Cold chain maintaining in food trade. *Food Control,* 17, 108–113.

Leitch, I., Blair, I.S. & McDowell, D.A. (2001). The role of environmental health officers in the protection of allergic consumers. International *Journal of Environmental Health Research,* 11, 51–61.

Marklinder, M., Lindbald, M., Eriksson, L. M., Finnson, A. M. & Lindqvist, R. (2004). Home storage temperatures and consumer handling of refrigerated foods in Sweden. *Journal of Food Protection,* 67(11), 2570–2577.

McCarthy, M., Brennan, M., Kelly, A. L., Ritson, C., De Boer, M. & Thompson, N. (2007). Who is at risk and what do they know? Segmenting a population on their food safety. *Food Quality and Preference,* 18(2), 205–217.

Mead, P.S., Slutsker, L., Dietz, V., McCaig, L.F., Bresee, J.S., Sharpio, C., Griffin, P.M. & Tauxe R.V. (1999). Food-related illness and death in the United States. *Emerging Infectious Diseases,* 5, 607-625.

Meer, R.R. & Misner, S.L. (2000). Food safety knowledge and behaviour of expanded food and nutrition education program participants in Arizona. *Journal of Food Protection,* 63(12), 1725–1731.

Medeiros, L.C., Hillers, V.N., Chen, G., Bergmann, V., Kendall, P. & Schroeder, M. (2004). Design and development of food safety knowledge and attitude scales for consumer food safety education. *Journal of the American Dietetic Association,* 104, 1671–1677.

Mensah, P., Armar-Klemesu, M., Yeboah-Many, D., Ablordey, A., Rikimaru, K., Taniguchi, K., Nkrumah, F. & Kamiya, H. (1995) Microbial quality of infant foods from peri-urban Ghana, *African Journal of Health Sciences* 2: 282–286.

Nauta, J.M., Litman, S., Barker, C.G. & Carlin, F. (2003). A retail and consumer phase model for exposure assessment of Bacillus cerus. *International Journal of Food Microbiology,* 83, 205–218.

Oosterom, J. (1998). The importance of hygiene in modern society. *International Biodeterioration and Biodegradation,* 41, 185–189.

Ovca and Jevšnik (2009) Maintaining a cold chain from purchase to the home and at home: Consumer opinions. *Food Control,* 20, 167–172.

Othman, M.N. (2007). Food Safety in Southeast Asia: Challenges Facing the Region *Asian Journal of Agriculture and Development,* 4(2), 83–92.

Patil, S.R., Morales, R., Cates, S., Anderson, D. & Kendal, D. (2004). An application of meta-analysis in food safety consumer research to evaluate consumer behaviours and practices. *Journal of Food Protection,* 67(11), 2587–2595.

Raspor, P. (2004). Opening ceremony. In. *Book of abstracts.* New tools for improving microbial food safety and quality. Biotechnology and molecular biology approaches, 12-16 September 2004, Portorož, Slovenia, pp. 3–4.

Raspor, P. (2006). Faces of foods on the world of food systems (Editorial). *Acta Alimentaria,* 35(3), 247–249.

Raspor, P. (2008). Total food chain safety: how good practices can contribute? *Trends of Food Science and Technology,* 19, 405–412.

Raspor, P. & Jevšnik, M. (2008). Good Nutritional Practice from Producer to Consumer. *Critical Reviews in Food Science and Nutrition,* 48:276–292.

Redmond, E.C & Griffith, C.J. (2003). Consumer food handling in the home: A review of food safety studies. *Journal of food protection,* 66, 130-161.

Regulation (EC) No 178/2002 of the European Parliament and of the Council of 28 January 2002 laying down the general principles and requirements of food law, establishing the European Food Safety Authority and laying down procedures in matters of food safety, OJ L 31, p.1.

Rocourt, J., Moy, G.,Vierk, K. & Schlundt, J. (2003). The present state of food-borne disease in OECD countries. World Health Organization, Food Safety Department, Geneva. Available on line: http://www.who.int/foodsafety/publications/foodborn_disease/en/OECD%20Final%20for%20WEB.pdf (23. 11. 2009).

Rusin, P., Orsoz-Coughlin, P. & Gerba, C. (1998). Reduction of fecal coliform and hetertotrophic plate count bacteria in the household kitchen and bathroom by disinfection with hypochlorite cleaners. *Journal of Applied Microbiology,* 85, 819 – 828.

Scott, E., Bloomfield, S.F. & Barlowk, C.G. (1982). An investigation of microbial contamination in the home. *The Journal of Hygiene,* 89, 279–293.

Scott, E. (1996). Foodborne disease and other hygiene issues in the home. *Journal of Applied Bacteriology,* 80, 5–9.

Sammarco, M.L., Ripabelli, G. & Grasso, G.M. (1997). Consumer attitude and awareness towards food-related hygienic hazards. *Journal of Food Safety,* 17, 215–221.

Smole Možina, S., & Hočevar Grom, A. (2004). Microbiological food safety. In L. Gašperlin & B. Žlender (Eds.), Food safety, 22. Bitencbitenčevi živilski dnevi, 18.-19.3.2004. Ljubljana, *Biotechnical faculty,* 29-43.

Surujlal, M. & Badrie, N. (2004). Household consumer food safety study in Trinidad, West Indies. *Internet Journal of Food Safety,* 3, 8–14.

Taulo, S., Wetlesen, A., Abrahamsen, R.K., Narvhus J.A. & Mkakosya, R. (2009). Quantification and variability of Escherichia coli and Staphylococcus aureus cross-contamination during serving and consumption of cooked thick porridge in Lungwena rural households, Malawi. *Food Control,* 20(12), 1158 – 1166.

Tauxe, R.V. (2002). Emerging foodborne pathogens. *International Journal of Food Microbiology,* 78, 31-41.

Terpstra, M.J., Steenbekkers, L.P.A., de Maetelaere, N.C.M. & Nijhuis, S. (2005). Food storage and disposal: Consumer practices and knowledge. *British Food Journal,* 107(7), 526–533.

Tom, P.D. (2006). Managing the cold chain for quality and safety. In: Seafood network information center. Available on line: http://seafood.ucdavis.edu/pubs/coldchain.doc (16. 06. 2006).

The ozfoodnet working group (2007). Monitoring the incidence and causes of diseases potentially transmitted by food in australia: annual report of the ozfoodnet network, 2007. Available on line: http://www.health.gov.au/internet/main/publishing.nsf/Content/cda-cdi3204-pdf-cnt.htm/$FILE/cdi3204c.pdf (28. 11. 2009).

Unusan, N. (2007). Consumer food safety knowledge and practices in the home in Turkey. *Food control,* 18(1), 45–51.

WHO (2003). The World Health Report 2003: Shaping the future, pp. 160, Geneva, World Health Organization. Available on line: http://www.who.int/whr/2003/en/.

WHO (2007). Food safety and health: a strategy for the who african region. Avalible on line: http://afrolib.afro.who.int/RC/RC%2057/Doc%20En/AFR-RC57-4.pdf (28.9.2008).

WHO (2008). Foodborne disease outbreaks: guidelines for investigation and control. http://whqlibdoc.who.int/publications/2008/9789241547222_eng.pdf (6. 12. 2009).

WHO (2009) Consumer Education. Prevention of foodborne disease: Five keys to safer food. http://www.who.int/foodsafety/consumer/5keys/en/index.html (16. 12. 2009).

Wilcock, A., Pun, M., Khanonax, J. & Aung, M. (2004). Consumer attitudes, knowledge and behaviour: a review of food safety issues. *Trends in Food Science & Technology,* 15, 56–66.

Yang, S., Angulo, F.J. & Altekruse, S.F. (2000). Evaluation of safe food-handling instructions on raw meat and poultry products. *Journal of Food Protection,* 63(10), 1321–1325.

INDEX

A

abuse, 1, 17, 18, 32
accounting, 10
adsorption, 18
advantages, 3
Africa, 7, 9, 10, 30
agencies, 23
antibiotic, 6
antibiotic resistance, 6
Asia, 10
assessment, 33
authorities, 6, 23

B

bacteria, 34
barriers, 3, 16, 25, 31, 32
basic needs, 27
bias, 25

C

Cameroon, 9
category d, 3
cholera, 10
climate, 21
color, iv
consumer education, 23
consumer protection, 11
consumption, 5, 13, 19, 27, 28, 35
contamination, 1, 2, 6, 11, 18, 19, 34, 35
cooking, 12
cooling, 19, 21
copyright, iv
correlation, 21
culture, 3

D

damages, iv
deaths, 8, 9, 10
Denmark, 2
destruction, 12
developing countries, 1, 5, 11
diarrhea, 9
disability, 10
disadvantages, 3
disinfection, 34
distress, 6
drawing, 16
drinking water, 5
durability, 16

E

ecology, 6
economic change, 6

economic losses, 6
economic status, 13
economy, 1, 5, 28
educational programs, 23
egg, 7, 10
environmental conditions, 18
epidemiology, 6
equipment, 27
etiology, 9
European Parliament, 30, 34
European Union, 5, 30
exposure, 16, 33

F

Finland, 2
fish, 20
flavor, 28
food habits, 1
food industry, 1, 5, 30, 32
food poisoning, vii, 19
food products, 20
food safety, vii, 3, 5, 11, 12, 13, 15, 16, 17, 18, 19, 20, 21, 23, 24, 25, 29, 30, 31, 32, 33, 34, 35
foodborne illness, 31
France, 2, 8

G

general practitioner, 7
Georgia, 9
globalization, 1, 6, 11, 20
GNP, 13, 16, 25
guidance, 6
guidelines, 18, 35

H

hazards, 1, 26, 29, 34
health problems, 24
health systems, 6
heat treatment, 20
hepatitis, 10
human resources, 25
Hungary, 2, 29
hygiene, 11, 16, 19, 23, 30, 32, 33, 34

I

Iceland, 2
ideal, 21
impacts, 32
incidence, 1, 5, 6, 9, 31, 35
ingestion, 5, 12
interface, 28
inventions, 27
Ireland, 2
isolation, 9

K

kindergartens, 10

L

legality, 3
legislation, 1, 27
Listeria monocytogenes, 21
low temperatures, 17, 20

M

majority, 8, 9, 19, 21, 27
management, 3, 32
marketing, 13
mass media, 5
meat, 7, 17, 20, 21, 29, 35
media, vii
messages, 6, 23
meta-analysis, 33
methodology, 3
Mexico, 9
misunderstanding, 16, 25
modeling, 18

modern society, 33
molecular biology, 34
monitoring, 7, 30
motivation, 16, 25
multiplication, 11

N

natural sciences, 27
neglect, 11, 16
Netherlands, 7
New Zealand, 2
Nigeria, 9
North America, 25
nutrition, 27, 28, 33

O

obesity, 27
opportunities, 19

P

pathogens, 5, 6, 7, 9, 12, 16, 21, 31, 35
performance, 31
peri-urban, 33
permission, iv, 2, 12, 13, 24
platform, 24, 25
Portugal, 29
poultry, 35
prevention, 31
probability, 18
producers, 16, 19, 23, 26, 28
psychology, 4
public health, 1, 4, 6

Q

qualitative research, 3
quality of life, 26

R

raw materials, 24
recommendations, iv
relatives, vii
reliability, 31
religion, 28
research and development, 27
resistance, 9
resources, 3
restaurants, 8
retail, 15, 16, 17, 20, 32, 33
rights, iv
risk assessment, 10
risk factors, 15
risk perception, vii

S

seafood, 20, 35
signals, 3
social life, 4
social sciences, 3, 27
social support, 31
social-psychological perspective, 29
South Africa, 9
Southeast Asia, 10, 33
Spain, 2, 8, 31
storage, 1, 15, 17, 18, 20, 21, 27, 28, 33, 35
supply chain, vii, 1, 3, 6, 10, 11, 13, 16, 20, 25, 27, 28
surveillance, 7, 9, 12, 31
survey, 17, 30, 31, 32
survival, 1, 2, 18
Sweden, 2, 33
symptoms, 6, 9
synchronization, 28

T

temperature, 1, 16, 17, 20, 21, 30, 32
test procedure, 29

testing, 6, 9
thermometer, 21
toxin, 8
training, 23, 25
transport, 17, 20
Turkey, 30, 35

U

United Kingdom, 2, 31

V

validation, 32
vegetables, 17, 20
video, 31
vision, 25

W

West Indies, 29, 34